The Tomb Guardians

Paul Griffiths

HENNINGHAM
FAMILY
PRESS

Paul Griffiths would like to thank:
Staff at the Alte Pinakothek, Munich
Staff at the York Art Gallery

First published in 2021 by Henningham Family Press
130 Sandringham Road, London, E8 2HJ
henninghamfamilypress.co.uk

Printed and bound by Short Run Press, Exeter
& Henningham Family Press, London
Cover printed on Gmund Bier Pils 250gsm
Gmund papers are manufactured near Munich

ISBN 9781916218611

The Tomb Guardians

Paul Griffiths

HENNINGHAM FAMILY PRESS

London

2021

for James Tookey

What are we going to do now?

I don't know what to do now.

What do you mean, What are we going to do now?

What do you mean?
I just don't know what to do.

Steady on.

Steady on.
You don't realise.

What's the problem, then?

What?

It's this lecture.

Yes.

I just don't like it.

It's fallen apart on me.

There's a lot I don't like, beginning with that dirty great rock having shifted on its own-i-o.

That's happened before.

He shouldn't have gone.

Not like this. The whole point.... Never mind.

No, he shouldn't have gone.

It's about the tomb guardians?

Nevertheless, he did.

Yes.

Those pictures of the tomb guardians?

Leave it.

The body's been placed in some kind of cave, which has been sealed with a stone, and they're there –

And they're there to make sure nothing happens. But it does. Total failure. I know the feeling.

How many of them are there?

It's not going to help to talk.

We're talking. How many of them are there?

It was better when there were the four of us.

Four.

Four was a good number.
So now we're three. What difference does it make?
We knew where we were, then.
And now we don't?

And they were standing guard, but –

Why did he have to go?
He'd've had his reasons.
He may have known.
Yes, he may have known.
Did he say anything to either of you? Before he left?
We were asleep. Remember?

They fell asleep.

He must've known. That's why he went. Obvious.
But did he say anything? Earlier on?
Not a word.

And the pictures?

I saw it coming.

Show them asleep.
All of them?

Yeah.

Yes.

I did. I saw it coming. There was something about him.

All four?

All four. But each one separately. On his own. Each of them asleep.

Be quiet.

You'd have expected them to take it in turns, wouldn't you? Two on, two off. After all, these are Roman legionaries. Professionals.

Never mind all that. What are we going to do now?

Maybe none of them wanted to miss it.

And so they all ended up missing it.

Exactly. Now can we talk about something else?

Hang on. He may have known, you say?

I want to know about these tomb guardians.

I told you, it's fallen apart.

That's it: he would've known.

Get it up on your laptop.

Not now.

You've involved me. You didn't have to. Get it up on your laptop and read the thing.

I start by introducing the topic –

Just read.

"My subject this evening is a set of three paintings by the sixteenth-century master Bernhard Strigel, housed in the Munich Alte Pinakothek – three paintings, each showing an armed man asleep on the ground. Three paintings, three portraits. Of course, the artist painted not three but four. The other one became separated at some point from the Munich trio."

What I'm wondering is: Where is he now? Where did he go to? And when did he go? And why ever did he think he had to go – and leave us?

Lost?

Obvious: he would've known.

No. It's somewhere else. I come to that.

You know, I think you're right. I think he must've known.
That's why he went. He knew, you see.
You mean he knew what was going to happen?
You think he was in on it? He was one of them?
Stands to reason.
So he goes...
He goes in case...

"They are asleep. The artist depicts them fully at their ease, while at the same time prompting in us disquiet, unease. We know what they are sleeping through, what they are not witnessing, even though this is their sole task, their sole purpose. We know what they are missing, which might very possibly be happening right at this moment, right here and now, in another part of the scene." That's the thing. Here we have these three, each of them alone, in these three pieces of a giant jigsaw, and we know there's one piece missing, the fourth of the group, and we know there's also a lot else missing. It's what these three, four men are missing. And what's missing in terms of the number of pictures. And what we, in our turn, are missing.

In case what?

In case he gets himself killed in the fracas. In the brouhaha.

But there wasn't any...of that.

Only because we were asleep! Look: Something happened. We know that. You reckon that stone moved by itself? Something happened. We missed it. Somebody came. More than one person, must've been, to shift that thing. We were supposed to stop that from happening. That's exactly what we were supposed to stop from happening. If we'd been awake, we'd have stopped it. We'd have stopped them. We'd probably have gone for them when we first heard them approaching. A whisper. The crack of a twig. We get up. We draw our weapons. We go in their direction. Silent, like. Come on, we can do this. We're professionals. Not a sound do we make. Not a sound. So we can catch them all unawares as they come out of the wood there. But of course

they're armed, too. There's a fight. Very likely some-
one gets himself killed. Now, he's just woken up, and
he's thinking all this, and the three of us are still
asleep. They're going to come, he thinks. There'll
be a fight. Someone'll get himself killed. Could be
him, he thinks. We're all dead to the world. Here's
his chance. So off he goes. Before it happens. Before
there's any danger of it happening.

Now you say all that, I don't see it.

You don't see it?

No. You want to know why? I know him. He's just not
like that. He's not one of them. He's a really great
guy.

Oh, well that's it then, isn't it? He's a great guy. End of
story.

You have a beginning. You know that.

You don't know him. Not the way I do. Did. We came
here together. Remember? We were one hundred
per cent inseparable. We were mates.

In that case, why isn't he here with you now, "insepa-
rable"?

Look, I'm not standing here –

Cut it out, you two. How well do you really know him,
either of you?

9

You're right. And remember this: we were asleep, all of us. We all fell asleep, pretty much at the same time, I would guess. We were asleep. What if there had been a noise, like you just said? A noise, and he was the only one of us to hear it. He has a choice now. He can wake the rest of us, us three here, but he thinks: No, can't do that, one of them'd be bound to say something, or groan, and then the game's up. So he goes by himself, doesn't he? He thinks: There aren't so many of them, only two or three by the sound of it, and I can take them by surprise in that patch of woodland, deal with them before they know what's happening. So off he goes, creeps away. He would've done that, taken it all on himself. That's the kind of thing he would do for you. I tell you: he's solid.

Solid and creeps away? If you say so. Only perhaps it doesn't turn out like he thought. Maybe there are more of them. Maybe they see him before he sees them.

What happens then?

That's not the problem.

"What happens then?" Come on, lad.

You mean he might be over there, somewhere in the wood?

What's left of him.

Anyway, he's gone.

You think we should go and look for him?

What would be the point? If he's lying over there, he's beyond needing anything we could do for him.

And if he's gone, he could be anywhere by now.

He could be back at the camp.

Go on, please.

He could indeed be back at the camp, telling his side of things, putting himself in the clear.

He wouldn't do that. He just wouldn't do that. I know him.

So you said.

I'm still tired.

Me too.

"Strigel gives us four sleeping soldiers, of whom in Munich we see only three, one being an absentee, not on parade. Three and a vacancy, where the fourth was, but is no longer. We have before us three men asleep – or rather three times one man asleep, each in his own square, his own space, his own little patch of the world." I thought this was so important, the sameness. Each of them asleep. Each of them separate from the others but out in the same landscape. They're like three Jacks in a pack of cards, the fourth not there.

Now look, this is no time to start nodding off again. We need to think about the mess we're in. Us. Not him. Us. Get it?

Carry on.

"We should pause for a moment to consider this matter of sleep in painting. There are the familiar examples – Seurat's drawing of a man prone to the ground – but I want to come at this from a perhaps more naive direction. As we wander through an art gallery, nearly all the people we see – the subjects, I mean, the permanent residents, not the visitors and the guards – will be awake. Consider the matter of a portrait. The sitter holds a pose of scrutiny made not for the artist but for us, the innumerable unknown viewers, down through the centuries. The sitter is looking the way the sitter wants to be seen looking – though of course the artist can mediate the effect. This is me. This is me being me. This is me trying to be me. This is me trying to show the me I want to

16

seem to be. A person asleep, however, is without self-presentation. There is an innocence." That's part of it, the innocence of the sleeper.

Could I say something?

Go on.

We can't be blamed for falling asleep.
Not sure about that....
No, he's right. We thought we'd be bound to wake up if there was any disturbance.
That's it: we had no idea it could all happen without a sound.

"But that innocence depends on their being alive, on there being no doubt of their being alive, and that is what is so remarkable in this instance, in these three instances, that the subjects are so obviously asleep and not dead. Strigel here is the first painter in the history of European art to strive for the naturalistic depiction of sleep. How can he make us know, he asks himself, that these men are still breathing? For the quality of innocence is immediately dispelled by death. Innocence is for the living. Guilt can survive death, but not innocence."

Come on, we were sent out here to stand guard!

"The innocence of sleep is the innocence of inaction, of a suspension from action, but also of vulnerability. These three have gone to sleep out of doors, out in the countryside, unprotected. They have left themselves confidently to the mercy of the world. But how does Strigel have us know that these –"

I don't like it. I just don't like it.

You mean, we should go away now, get out of here, before anyone else…?

I mean, it is our fault. We're responsible. We can be held responsible. We neglected our duty. We fell asleep.

You don't have to put it that way.

Don't I? Isn't that what happened?

Do you think there's any chance they'll forget about us?

Yeah, they've probably forgotten already.

Are you all right?

Have either of you two had a sudden accident or something? Forget about us? You don't seem to understand. This is political. This is hot. A local rebel got executed. The population's full of his partisans. They'll want to get their revenge. Almost certainly it's some of them have taken the body. And we – us lot, all four of us – were supposed to stop that from happening. Oh yes, they'll forget about us, all right. Sure, they'll forget about us.

"– that these men are indeed sleeping and not dead? One clue would be that they are, as I said, out of doors – but not on a battlefield, with no sign of a wound and their weapons seemingly unused. More to the point, theirs are clearly living bodies, with working muscle; they have their knees raised."

I suppose it's not very likely.

No.

You reckon they did take the body, then?

What do you think? The tomb, over there, the tomb we were told to keep an eye on, lies open. Observe: the stone at its entrance, set in place and sealed, has been rolled away. Oh yes, you say, perhaps somebody came back because there was something they'd forgotten to put in – like a pair of numskulls.

"And their innocence is accentuated, made all the more vivid, we may say, by those unguarded weapons lying on the ground."

Don't be like that.

They didn't take any of our stuff, though, did they?

No.

No.

That's all right then.

We're in the clear.

In the clear!? We are in big trouble, my friend. Big, big trouble. If that body's been taken away – and what's the likelihood it hasn't? – they'll want an explanation. Four men there to guard a dead Judæan – and they can't even do that!

You think? I don't reckon anyone'll care. They only sent us out here because of some kerfuffle these priests were making. Nobody cared. You could see that when the cent gave us our instructions. Smirk on his face. Have to put on a bit of a show for the sake of the locals, they'd told him. Just a few men'll do. Not your crack troops, needless to say.

Excuse me! We may not be from one of your premier attack legions, but we are trained, and we are skilled, and we have clean records, and we've been chosen to deal with a difficult situation here. Dangerous, even. We're not your bottom-of-the-barrel men.

We're not! We're strong. We're clear-headed –

We fell asleep.

Anyone could do the same.

Come on! Anyway, if this mission was so important, perhaps they do care after all, which might mean they're going to ask some awkward questions if we turn up unannounced.

We'll think of something.

Oh, great! "We'll think of something." That's wonderful. That's a big help.

Go on.

I'm scared.

Me too.

We've been here too long.

That's all it is.

No, it's this place: all these tombs, all these spirits wandering about, searching for living bodies to move into, feel their legs move again, feel the breath coming out of their mouths again, hear themselves speak.

Quiet!

Yeah, give over! You think too much; that's the trouble with you.

And we've been here too long. I don't like it. Sooner or later they're going to send somebody out here, and then what?

Maybe we should go back to the camp now, before they come for us.

And say what? That's the question.

Maybe we should just scarper, like he did.

If he did.

That's right. We don't know what happened to him now, do we?

We'll have to go back some time, but we've got to work out what to say first.

We missed it.

Whatever it was.

"We missed it." Not much of a story, is it? "Oh," says the cent, "and why did you miss it?" "We fell asleep."

"But it is all going to be very different when they wake

up. They missed it. This is all they can think about. They missed it, and they are responsible – not only for having missed it but for its having happened, as they probably see it. They were on duty, and what did they do? They fell asleep, allowing the body to be taken away. They are going to have to work out what to say. Things are not looking too good for them, and they are going to have to come up with some kind of explanation."

What are we going to do then?
We can't say what really happened.

How much do we actually know, from the sources?

No, because we don't know what really happened.
No, I mean we can't say we fell asleep.
Er, no.
Therefore, we have to make up a story.
So we do.
Something that's not true? Something that never happened?
That does seem to be what we need.
I'm not very happy about that.

What else can we do?

Not much.

*Let's just consider our situation. Some people might say
    this was an easy assignment, keeping check on a
    dead body. But they'd be wrong.*

They would.

*We needed to be firm in our resolve yet sensitive to local
    customs. We needed to –*

Stay awake.

Right, we needed to stay awake.

And we fell asleep.

How much is not much?

*Right, we fell asleep. Can't be argued with. We fell
    asleep.*

We slipped up.

We slipped up, yes.

And now we don't know what to do.

Let's rather say we're thinking what to do.

I'll skip forward to that bit, if you like. "The whole matter of placing a guard on the tomb is mentioned in only one of the gospels, Matthew, and there are very few details."

How long do we have to go on thinking?
You know, I'm worried.
Me too.

"Matthew Twenty-seven, verse sixty-two. King James Version. 'Now the next day, that followed the day of the preparation, the chief priests and Pharisees came together unto Pilate, Saying, Sir, we remember that that deceiver said, while he was yet alive, After three days I will rise again. Command therefore that the sepulchre be made sure until the third day, lest his disciples come by night, and steal him away, and say unto the people, He is risen from the dead: so the last error shall be worse than the first. Pilate said unto them, Ye have a watch: go your way, make it as sure as ye can. So they went, and made the sepulchre sure, sealing the stone, and setting a watch.'"

That's not going to get us anywhere. We need to have a plan.

A plan.

Yes, we need to come up with a plan.

Maybe one of us goes back, with some story we've all agreed on. Some reason why it's just the one of us coming back.

Might be two of us, if he's already reported in.

Well, that's part of our problem. We don't actually know what situation we're in. It could be that a party is on its way out here right now to take us in and put us on a charge.

Could be. I don't like this at all.

Calm down, calm down. Remember your training. Think. Know. Act.

Right. Think. Know. Act.

For a start, let's think what we know.

How long have we been here?

Good one. How long have we been here?

So the guard wasn't placed until the day after the entombment?

Two days?

Correct, according to this account.

Seems like forever.

In that case, it could all have happened during the first
   night, before the tomb was sealed, and before the
   soldiers were on the scene?

Less.
Less than forever?

It could, but it didn't. Otherwise they'd all have
   known in Jerusalem. They'd have heard the claims
   that were being made by the man's followers.
   Pilate acts as soon as he's alerted to the danger
   of deceit and misrepresentation. If that's already
   happened – or let's just say if the story's already
   broken – he'll know. So will these chief priests
   and Pharisees who come to see him and put in
   their request. They wouldn't be doing that. They
   wouldn't be asking.

I believe it was only yesterday, as a matter of straightfor-
   ward fact.

Sure.

No: night before last we came. Then there was all of yesterday. And now this morning.

There'd be no point.

But remember: it was already light when we got here. We've only been here through the one night.

Of course.

You're right.
I don't really remember....

So Pilate gives them a guard,

Come on, you do remember getting shaken awake and marched off out here.

to prevent something happening that hasn't yet happened.

If you say so. But where's this getting us?

Watch.

No, he's right.

What?

It's just been the one night. That's all.

You said "watch" before. And Pilate didn't give them
the watch. They already had it. According to what
you quoted. From Matthew.

Wasn't like this when it got dark last night.

Sorry, I'm starting to get anxious.

What wasn't?

"Ye have a watch", if I remember correctly.

*Oh dear, let me see now.... Whatever can I have been
thinking of? The tomb, idiot!*

Watch....

Give it a rest, we're just trying to work things out.
    Together.
Yeah, we're just trying to remember what happened so's
    we can build up our story.

What is it in the Greek?

There ain't nobody's going to help us out.
No.
There ain't nobody's going to be on our side in this one.
You don't have to tell me.

I don't care any more what it is in the Greek!

So we need to get our facts straight.
Right.
That's all we're trying to do at the moment.
Wait a minute, though. Who put you in command?
Leave off, will you!

Sorry. Please read on. Take a pause, if you like.

Look, we're all getting rattled. We're all on edge. We don't know what's going on here. We don't know what's happened. We don't know what might be going to happen. And we've only ourselves to rely on.

Nobody else is going to look out for us.

We're on our own.

So let's just try to stay calm, and not take it out on each other.

Let's just try to put together what we know.

Yes.

And let's have that go for all three of us, please.

I said I'm sorry.

I heard you.

Let's start out with the basics.

Right.

Item: We were woken up the night before last and brought out here by the cent and a couple of new recruits who then went back to the barracks.

"This is how Matthew tells us – and remember he is our only source, from among the traditional gospels – that a guard is placed on the tomb."

Hang on, we don't know that for sure.

We don't know what for sure?

That they went back to the barracks after the cent had posted us here.

Oh, sorry. It's difficult, sometimes, to know what you know and what you don't, what you're only supposing on the basis of what you do know, but in fact you don't know, you only think you know, if you know what I mean.

So, Item: We were woken up the night before last and brought out here by the cent and a couple of new recruits who then went away again.

We know roughly when it was, too, don't we? It was just beginning to get light, so, late in the fourth watch.

Right you are. So again, Item: We were woken up the night before last some time late in the fourth watch and brought out here by the cent and a couple of new recruits who then went away again.

We had some food with us: remember that.

And shouldn't we say there were four of us?

Item: The four of us were woken up the night before last

some time late in the fourth watch and brought out
here with a supply of food and water enough for two
or three days by the cent and a couple of new recruits
who then went away again.

"'So they went, and made the sepulchre sure, sealing
the stone, and setting a watch.'"

Item: We sealed the stone, as instructed.
I don't remember sealing any stone.

The implication is that the "they" here are the people
who've gone to see Pilate: the chief priests and
Pharisees – not that they would have done it
personally, of course, but that they oversaw the
stone sealing and set the watch.

Not us personally, no. But we saw it done, I mean.
Did we?
Not that I remember.
Nor me.

How?
How what?

How would the stone have been sealed? Archaeological evidence?

Perhaps we should leave out how they sealed the stone.
Good idea.

I have no idea.

Not our job.

I'm sorry.

You're right there. They'll expect us to stick to what we did ourselves.

I've got to ask you not to introduce detours.

Yes, we should stick to what <u>we</u> did <u>ourselves</u>.
We can just leave it out, then, about the stone being sealed.
I don't agree.

No. Of course. I'm sorry.

Me neither. It needs to be there. It might be important. Later on, I mean.

He's right.

You're not wrong. Item: The tomb was sealed.

The entrance to the tomb was sealed.

The entrance to the tomb was blocked with a stone, which was sealed in place.

Item: The entrance to the tomb was blocked with a stone, which was sealed in place.

Good.

Very good.

Item: We kept watch through the day. Nobody came.

Somebody went.

What did you say?

I said: I'm sorry.

Somebody went.

Somebody went, we're saying?

Somebody went. Item: –

Hang on: I'm not sure we need go into that.

No, it might cause problems for him if we put it into any kind of official record.

"As to the essential moment, the event, of the man's rising from the dead, it is again only Matthew who comes near recounting what happened."

We're not talking about an official record. We're just trying to get the facts sorted out, for our own benefit.

"'And, behold, there was a great earthquake: for the angel of the Lord descended from heaven, and came and rolled back the stone from the door, and sat upon it. His countenance was like lightning, and his raiment white as snow: And for fear of him the keepers" – that is, the people who concern us – "did shake, and became as dead men.' No mention of the one coming out of the tomb."

Right you are, we'll leave him out of it.
It's probably better that way.
I'm sure it is.
All agreed? Then let's continue.

"We learn what must have happened to him only as the first visitors learn. There is no body. A heavenly agency has intervened."

Item: As night began to fall we formed a plan.
Whoa, can we please discuss this a bit?

"As to the –"

Yes, we should be very careful what we say here.

"As to the soldiers sent to stand guard, Matthew indic-
      ates that they didn't just drift off but were shocked
      into sleep by the appearance of the angel."

*We can't say we all just fell asleep. Anyone would say we
      should've been taking it in turns. Anyone would say
      that.*

"Now how does Strigel deal with this? Observe this
      fellow here, seated on the ground, resting his head
      on his left palm while his right arm dangles."

*Did we try taking it in turns? Did any of us suggest
      that?*
Wait.

"Look at him, with his half-open mouth."

We have to be very careful here, even in what we say just to each other, because you say something, and somebody else'll remember it, and then little by little it becomes the truth, you know, it becomes the story, it becomes what we all of us remember, even if it never happened that way at all.

"Does he look as if he's dead? Does he look as if he's been literally shaken to death? Or does he look as if he's just peacefully in the land of Nod?"

You're right.

We did not fall asleep. Everybody got that? No way did we fall asleep, not all of us at once.

That's right.

We kept watch. We did as we were instructed.

Yeah.

Better be sure we did.

Not all of us all the time through the night, of course.

No.

Couldn't have.

Two of us at a time, while the other two rested. We kept watch.

That's the story.

No, and never forget this: that's the fact. Item: We kept watch through the night, two on, two off.

So how come they got away with it, then?

How come who got away with what?

Rolled the stone. Took away the body.

Hang on, we don't know that for sure, do we?

Want to check?

No fear!

Nor me! I'm not going near any tomb!

"Where, if we follow Matthew, we would expect to see the appearance of death, instead we can almost hear this man's deep breathing. Where we would expect evidence of a recent violent attack, of heaven crashing into earth and splaying the bystanders, we have pastoral. Strigel shows his subjects calmly sleeping, each dreaming his own dream."

Got it.

What?

There was a Supernatural Event.

You what?

A Supernatural Event, stupid.

"Before dealing with this, we should ask ourselves how it was that Matthew, or whoever wrote his gospel for him, knew what these four men at arms had experienced. Mary Magdalene and 'the other Mary' were present as well, we remember, but, with an earthquake occurring and an angel descending, we can hardly imagine they would have been giving any attention to the soldiers standing guard – members of the occupying force; men."

We didn't hear anything, did we? If some of his followers had come, if they'd pushed back the rock –

After breaking the seals.

– after breaking the seals, we'd've heard something. We'd've woken up.

Always assuming we'd been asleep.

Which we weren't.

Which we weren't.

Ergo, it all happened in complete and total silence. Ergo, it was a Supernatural Event.

Wait on, though. We weren't asleep, right? Not all of us.

Right.

At least one of us, at any given time, has his eyes on the tomb.

For sure.

We keep a fire going, so there's some light.

I think I see where you're going.

Right. Even if there's no sound, none at all, the rock can't be moved away without someone who's watching being able to see it – being able to see your Supernatural Event.

Mmmm.

Well then, try this. Thunder and lightning. An earthquake. We're all awake now, and we see...

Yes?

The divine Cautes descending from the skies. He thrusts a finger towards us, points at us one by one, and one by one we topple over, zonked. By the time we come to, it's all over. The stone has been rolled away and the tomb is empty.

It's a good question.

And in fact Matthew himself goes on to answer it.

I like it.

But we shouldn't say anything about the tomb being empty.

"'Some of the watch came into the city," he tells us, "and shewed unto the chief priests all the things that were done.'"

We don't know that.

And we're not about to look.

I think we can assume that's what's happened here. Otherwise why'd they meddle with the tomb if they're not going to take the body away? Why go to all the trouble of heaving away that stone? So: Item: At one point in the night there was thunder and lightning and an earthquake, which woke up the two of us who were sleeping, so that we all saw the divine Cautes descending from the skies, but not for too long, because thunderbolts from him knocked all of us out cold, one by one, and when we came to again we saw that the stone had been rolled aside and the tomb left empty.

That'll do all right.

I'm still not sure....

You're saying that through the chief priests, the soldiers' story could have become common knowledge.

Yes, but look: do you really want to go on with this?

Yes. Please. You can't stop now.

O.K., but I reserve the right –

Go on.

"According to this account in Matthew, only they – besides the two women known to be close associates of the man in question – had witnessed at least the prelude to the supreme event."

Sounds good to me.

"It would have been in their interests to tell their story, in order to exonerate themselves."

This'll get us off the hook all right.

"Matthew, then, hears the same story from the women who found the tomb empty and from the soldiers who had been on guard. If we accept scholarly consensus and place the writing of this gospel much later in the first century, we could imagine one of these soldiers as an old man – this might be forty or fifty years afterwards, and we find him sitting outside the villa he has bought with his pension, on the outskirts of Caesarea, as with his right arm stretched out he tells his tale to someone who listens and remembers."

That's how it happened. Are we all agreed?

"To the possible objection that the soldiers (or, at any rate, this particular soldier) might have made the whole thing up – earthquake, angel, the lot – we can answer that our concern is not with the veracity of the gospel story but rather with the work of Bernhard Strigel, who, given his place and period, would have been bound to accept, at least publicly, the factual accuracy of that story."

Agreed.

I just want to –

And I'll vote yes on behalf of our absent friend.

"At this point we may tackle the conundrum I mentioned just now, that the images Strigel presents, of slumbering contentment, jar more than somewhat with the story in Matthew that the watchkeepers shook with fear and, I quote, 'became as dead men'."

Do we need to go any further?

You'd better be sure we do!

"We have been proceeding as if Strigel's paintings were illustrations of the gospel story – specifically, of the story in Matthew."

No. I'm sorry, both of you, but I can't go along with this. One thing is, so far we've been sticking to the facts. That's what you said we should do, stick to the facts. Now we're making something up that never happened.

"Each of these pictures, however, has other tales it tells."

It could've done.

"For this was a story recounted in many more ways than the four gospels allow."

Come on. Please. Who's going to believe this rigmarole? They're going to see through it right away. They're going to see we've just made up some fancy story to cover ourselves, when what really happened was that we all, like babes in arms, just drifted off byebyes and somebody, person or persons unknown, came along, rolled away that boulder –

After breaking the seals.

– after breaking the seals, and took the body away.

"To repeat, Matthew alone of those four mentions the
watchers at the tomb."

Just one problem.
What?

"There were, however, other gospels, accounts that were
rejected when the canonical scriptures came to be
put together, somewhere in the fourth century,
long after anyone could have had any reliable
connection with an eye-witness, when all they
had to go on were the written records. These they
judged not by their verisimilitude but according
to whether or not they agreed with the theology
that had become established."

I grant you, this is what must have happened.

"There are dozens of them – though most were vigor-
ously suppressed a full millennium before Strigel
and almost all copies of them zealously destroyed.
Some, however, escaped, if only in part, and there
remains the possibility that others may yet come

to light. After two thousand years, the story is not yet finished."

I'll go further: this is what must have happened – makes me think I've been underestimating these Judæans if they could shift that thing. But it relies on us being asleep.

Which we weren't.

Which we most certainly weren't.

"As we explore that story's various branches, we find others in which our subjects make an appearance."

So there's our choice. Either we tell them what really happened, what must have happened, what did happen, which means we have to say we slept through the whole thing – "dereliction of duty", they'll call it – or we make up a story. But I agree: it'd better be a good story, solid, convincing.

"The gospel ascribed to the apostle Peter would be one."

And you think yours is?

"Among several, I should make clear."

You think you could do better?

"Not only does this narrative clarify the question of
whether or not Pilate supplied the guard – he did
– it gives us a bit more information, telling us this
guard consisted of 'Petronius the centurion with
soldiers'. So now we have a leader plus some others,
Roman infantry."

Yes, I'll have a go.

"Peter also tells us that this military party goes out to
the tomb with 'the elders and scribes', that everyone gets together to roll the stone and seal it, with
seven seals, and – this is the implication, at least
– that they all remain on site. They pitch a tent."

We've been on our own here all this time, right?

"As well they might, on a desert night."

*Yes, since the cent and those two lads left after bringing
us here.*

Right you are, somebody else came along, late last night.

"Through the night, according to this text, the soldiers 'were keeping guard two by two in every watch'."

No they didn't.

"This would, of course, allow for a contingent of four, but we are still not told the number."

This is the story, get it? Somebody else came along.

"'There came a great sound in the heaven, and they saw the heavens opened and two men descend thence, shining with a great light, and drawing near unto the sepulchre. And that stone which had been set on the door rolled away of itself and went back to the side, and the sepulchre was opened and both of the young men entered in.'"

It was one of their women. They sent one of their women so's we wouldn't immediately suspect trouble and give it one to any intruder.

"We might think the 'great sound' would have been enough to wake up anyone in range who was asleep, but according to this account the two who are on duty then rouse the centurion and the others – the elders and scribes are still there, we are told – so that everyone is awake to see what happens next."

They sent a woman so's we wouldn't do that; we'd be caught off guard.

I'm with you.

So along she comes, all humble, stooping over, whispering "Sirs! Sirs! Sirs!", or at least what we take to be "Sirs! Sirs! Sirs!" in her language, from the way she's acting, and holding out a jug of wine.

I can see it.

Go on, then.

Go on.

"Just as these two are telling the rest what they have seen – and surely they are pointing to the open tomb, and everyone can see the celestial light blazing out from it – 'three men come out of the sepulchre, two of them sustaining the other one, and a cross following, after them.'"

Well, there's two of us awake, see? That's the arrangement: two on, two off. We take a swig. Good stuff.

Better than we normally get. Much. So let's make a party. We wake the other two, and now we're all passing it around, and starting to feel jolly, despite the surroundings – except that she, she doesn't have any. We ask her to join us, but she says no – or that's what we understand her to be saying, at any rate.

One thing.

What?

"'And of the two they saw that their heads reached unto heaven, but of him that was led by them that it overpassed the heavens. And they heard a voice out of the heavens saying: Hast thou preached unto them that sleep? And an answer was heard from the cross, saying: Yea.'"

A woman comes out alone at night for a drinking party with four soldiers....

Got you. Right, they send a boy.

Goodness! Colossal beings, a voice from heaven, a speaking cross –

And that word 'sleep'. On the writer's mind.

Right.

Remember: the canonical gospels all pass over this crucial moment when the man, restored to life, exits his tomb.

Do they now?

Remind me.

Good point. We'll have it be an old man, with a stick.

And he has this whacking great jug of wine in the other hand, does he?

Look, can we work out the details later? All I'm trying to suggest is that we're drugged.

Drugged?

The nearest we get is that passage in Matthew, who gives us the earthquake and the angel on the rock, causing alarm and confusion among the soldiers and the arriving women. This would seem to be

the decisive moment, and yet absolutely nothing
at all is said about the one in the tomb.

*The wine's loaded with something, and now we're all
dead to the world, can't see the others of them
coming along, pushing the stone away –*

After breaking the seals.

– going in and absconding with the body.

I like it.

*I don't. Number one: whoever they send – man, woman,
child or hedgehog – we would have to be on our
guard, ready to deal with them one way or the other.
And number two: this settling down to have a drink
with one of the natives, it makes us look like fools.*

Really? I had no idea.

But there are two problems with this version, as I go
on to say.

Go on.

"Vivid as Peter's account may be, it must seem unlikely
to have any relevance to the Bernhard Strigel
paintings. In the first place, Peter does not have

the soldiers all asleep at the same time; as good watchmen would, they take turns. Also, the Gospel of Peter was not, of course, included in the official Bible, as determined by synods in Rome and Carthage in the late fourth century; it had been denounced long before that. We know copies went on being made, because one in fragmentary condition, from the eighth or ninth century, was discovered in Egypt in 1886. That, which happily includes the tomb episode, is still all we have. The translation I just quoted, by the way, was made by Montague Rhodes James."

I'm thinking. I'm listening to myself.
Hope you're making some sense, then.

You're arguing it cannot have been known to Strigel. By his time it'd been buried in the sands of Egypt for half a millennium.

How much longer are you going to be listening to yourself for?

It had.

Will you be quiet? I'm trying to sort out a problem.

Then, as I think you said before, it can't have had any bearing on the Strigel paintings.

We could tell them the truth.

I didn't quite say that.

Thank you.

No?

The problem is this, as far as I can make out: how to account for none of us knowing what happened if all the time two of us, at least, were awake.

"As I just noted, Peter has the soldiers keeping orderly watch. Indeed, none of the sources, whether accepted into the canon or not, absolutely none, have the men who are supposed to be on guard just calmly falling asleep, blissfully unaware of the event when it comes."

They were looking the other way.

Thanks again.

"In the canonical gospels, as we have seen, the whole
    event is drastically underplayed. There is only that
    verse in Matthew where the man must be leaving
    his tomb, but even then we are not told so."

*No, they were looking the other way. It was one of the na-
    tives, drawing their attention. Subterfuge. They're
    tricky, these Judæans.*

Sure are.

"It is as if, while reading, we fell asleep for a moment
    and missed it."

Very tricky.

*One of them comes up to us, waving an arm – a woman,
    a boy, an old man – and starts telling us some story.*

What story?

It's a long one.

"Does this mean, then, that Strigel had no basis for his
    sleeping soldiers?"

Yes?

"On the contrary."

*It's a long one, and it has to do with how some of them
    are planning to come out and steal the body. He's an
    informer, see. Or she. He or she has heard a couple
    of them talking about this plan in a tavern, where
    he or she, as it might be, is a waiter.*

Or waitress.

*There they are, sitting in this tavern, around a table,
    their heads down, but their eyes looking at each
    other, intently like, because this is a big thing for
    them, and they want to make sure they're all in it
    together, that one of them doesn't go off and tell the
    authorities –*

Us.

*– us – what they're up to. They're going to come out here
    and take away the body. This waiter, or waitress,
    was going up to the table with three or four foaming
    cups –*

Of what?

*– doesn't matter – and heard some crucial words, crucial
    words, like... let me think...*

"Body"?

Yeah, "body".

Doesn't matter, and so he or she went back to whisper a word to his or her boss, who gives him or her permission, saying: sure, get yourself up there right away, because he doesn't want to get caught – does he? – this boss, doing anything that might give assistance to this group of misfits sitting making his place look...

Lowering the tone.

Exactly, lowering the tone.... Where was I?

"For although there was nothing in the written record, there was a long tradition of depicting the soldiers as sleeping."

It's all right, we get the picture.

"For centuries the actual event was not depicted. There was no description in the Holy Book, which was the Word of God, and so there was nothing to illustrate."

This informer, with his eyes drawing us in, or her eyes, is pitching us this longwinded story, while exactly

what he's talking about as being planned, or she is,
is going on right there and then behind our backs.

That's it.

"And in the Orthodox Church it remains the case that
the event cannot be pictured."

In silence.

Yes.

Pushing the stone away in silence.

"But even though for a long time there were, on doc-
trinal grounds, no images of an angel rolling away
the stone, or floating men in white, or the figure
at the centre of it all climbing out of the tomb..."

Yes.

Yes?

"...the sleeping soldiers were already there."

It won't wash.

You have some examples?

*They brought some cloths with them – they thought it all
out in advance – so they brought some cloths with
them to lay on the ground and muffle the sound as
they moved the rock.*

I'll show a few. "Among the earliest representations
of them is a bas-relief from one of the Roman
catacombs, middle of the fourth century, with a
banner and two slumped soldiers at the foot of it."

Nice try, but we were sitting over there right by the thing.

Two, you say?

*He beckons us away. Or she does. Beckons us away.
Why do we go?*

Just the pair. But you have to reckon how much an
artist is constrained by the truth, or what's believed to be the truth, and how much by good
design. A matching pair. Book-ends.

Because this informer is indicating that he or she is going to show us the route they're taking to get here – over there, as it might be – and we go and check it out.

Symmetry.

Except it's as if this artist wanted to show a moment of change, and so has one of them still clearly asleep while his companion's looking up, alerted to what's going on.

So we're all over there looking the way this so-called informer is pointing –

Snake in the grass. I don't like him.

Or her.

"We also have an ivory belt-buckle from Provence, from the fifth century. This belonged to a sainted bishop and again shows two soldiers, one on each side of a sepulchre."

Oh well, if it's a woman....

"And now both of them are asleep."

I'm worried.

Why?

I don't think it shows us in a very good light again.

You could say we've abandoned our post.

You could say how two of us should've stayed on guard here while the other two went to see what this woman had to say for herself.

Or man.

Himself.

You could say we should've been more suspicious, of someone appearing in the dark, all out of nowhere.

"What I would like to propose here is something like the beginning of a tradition."

I see what you mean.

"A tradition of showing the guards asleep at their post."

Yeah.

You could say we failed in our duty.

"These objects of the fourth and fifth centuries come

from right at the moment when the canon of scripture is being fixed."

You could.

"Many gospels, perhaps hundreds, are being vehemently rejected."

We're in for it.

"Henceforth there are going to be four stories, and four only. Fluidity, variety, nuance are giving way to dogma."

We're surely in for it.

"The failed gospels are being destroyed, every scrap of them that can be found."

I think we should just leave all this alone for a bit.

"But perhaps ideas from them could survive – not in

words, because that would have been far too dangerous, but in images."

And see what occurs to us when we're not beating our brains to think up possible excuses.

Explanations.

"Perhaps a whole legacy of interpretation and reinterpretation could be conveyed, without words, in the work of artists down through the generations, in statues, robes, liturgical vessels, architectural details, devotional jewellery, embroidered altarcloths, monstrances, table tombs, reliquaries and all the rest of the paraphernalia, all the way to paintings done by a German artist in the early sixteenth century, our Bernhard Strigel."

Excuses.

How about one of us takes a look inside now?

"Looking at these images, we begin to hear muted voices."

Inside what?

The tomb, dummy!

"Consider the topic of the Madonna and Child. There was a way of showing this that had nothing to do with gospel accounts but came entirely from artists following what previous artists had done. So it is with our sleepers at the tomb. Nobody was saying they slept; everyone was showing they slept."

Ha, ha. Very funny.
Then we won't know what we're dealing with.

"Of course, a lot of the evidence will have been destroyed."

I don't want to know what I'm dealing with.
Nor me, thank you very much.

"But once we arrive at the age of detachable paintings – things that could withstand use and survive a church being redecorated – we find sleeping soldiers all over the place. And quite soon, by early in the fifteenth century, there is general agreement on there being four."

So are we three just going to sit here forever?

"This was, of course, a full century before our paintings."
And now I need a break.

Somebody'll come.

Of course.

Sooner or later.
And then what're we going to say?
We have time to think more about that.
Meanwhile, what're we going to do?
Nothing.
And when we've done all the nothing we can do?
We'll think of something.
And if we don't?
Stop asking questions! I don't know. I don't know.
Look, you two: calm down. We've got to stick together.
What about him?
What "him"?
The him that left, stupid.
Forget about him. I don't know why he wouldn't have
suggested we all go at the same time. But he didn't,
and that's that. He went. He left the story.

I tell you, he'd've had his reasons.

Whether or not, we should all have gone together. When he did. That was the time to go. We should all have gone together. Given up on it. Don't you think? We should all have gone together. Otherwise, otherwise, the whole thing's changed, hasn't it? He, by going, did something for himself. He left. He got away. I'm not criticizing. Good luck to him, wherever he is. But he also did something to us. We became the ones left behind. That may not have been his intention, I grant you, but that's what's happened. We were here on duty. We had a purpose here. Now we've just been left here.

Right.

You're not wrong.

You're all right?

I know I'm not wrong.

You're even right, in a way.

Fine. Let's get going again. "If we return now to the pictures by Strigel –"

He shouldn't have left.

Excuse me, but could we take a look at another of
  them on your laptop?

I've told you: Forget about him.

Here we are.
And this is again one of the three in Munich?

I've forgotten already.

Yes. "Each of the paintings shows a man sleeping, a
  soldier, and they are all the same size, around a
  half a metre square."

Good man.

"Within those constraints, however, Strigel has made
  them distinct characters. They could have been
  painted from life."

He was my friend, though.

"Even so, note that Strigel does not show us much of
  their faces."

You're right there: "was".

"If they were indeed painted from life, you might not
    recognize the models when you saw them out and
    about in the town."

You know –

Which town?

*Look, can we all just keep quiet for a bit? Use our ears
    and not our mouths for a change? Just listen out for
    anyone coming?*

Memmingen. It's in the south-west of Germany – a
    small place, but big enough to give employment
    to an artist, a painter, right from an earlier time.
    Whatever you could have wanted in the way of
    painting, there in Memmingen in the middle of
    the fifteenth century – church decoration, house
    decoration, a portrait if you were wealthy, an inn
    sign perhaps – Hans Strigel was the fellow for
    the job. That's our man's grandfather. There must
    have been thousands like him all over Europe, not
    so much artists as artisans, proudly showing off
    their skills and their training to the admiration

of the locals, and of course, as tradesmen will, passing on those skills to the next generation. One of Hans's sons, Ivo, went to Italy and came back a master sculptor in wood. Then in the next generation we arrive at the superlative artistry of Bernhard Strigel."

You know what I could do with right now?

"He doesn't seem to have travelled to study like Ivo; he had all he needed right there in Memmingen, with his father and his uncle to guide him. No inn signs in his studio, though, one would guess, once he got going. The portraits he made – a couple of dozen have survived – indicate his name was known a hundred miles from Memmingen, by notabilities who would probably send a messenger to summon him, and he would go, his paints and his brushes and some clothes strapped in bags to his horse, and he would be treated on his arrival with more or less grace, fed and lodged more or less generously, and the picture would be done, or perhaps two for a newly married couple, and he would receive his fee and go back home, as he had come, taking with him not the picture or pictures, of course, but what he had learned. The pictures they could keep. The pictures meant nothing to him. They were like the shells or skins that an animal must successively discard, as it grows. What mattered to him was what the painting had taught him – what the painting of the painting had taught him."

Date of birth?

A plate of bean soup.

Around 1460. "He may have gone for additional study to nearby Ulm, a bigger place than Memmingen, with a richer artistic tradition. However it was, wherever it was, he became expert in both the kinds of work for which there was a demand: religious paintings – especially altarpieces – and portraits. In a way, the paintings with which we are concerned exemplify both."

For me it'd have to be a cold beer. A real cold beer, picked out of a stream where it'd been dunked for a good bit. This climate...

Quite.

Quiet!

"He must have made more than a local reputation by 1504, when the Habsburg emperor Maximilian summoned him to paint a group portrait."

I'll take both.

"He was called back to the imperial court twice more. Maximilian must have liked his work."

Where d'you come from, then?

"And yet it's entirely possible he never actually saw the emperor."

You wouldn't have heard of it.
Try me.

"All his portraits of Maximilian look much the same, which could be because he had to base them on an earlier picture, the emperor being too busy to sit again."

Moridunum.

"Maximilian had a definite image of himself he wanted to convey. What he wanted seen – what he wanted shown – was his profile, like a head on a gold coin. We could imagine he had a model portrait to be shown to the next artist he'd had summoned."

Give it a rest, you two.

"Strigel always has him displaying the right side of his face, looking towards the left – towards the future, if we are reading from left to right."

You're right, I haven't heard of it.

Hey, I said: Give it a rest. And remember the rule. No pasts. You join the army, you forget all about where you came from and who you left behind, your parents, your sister, your girlfriend. That's all gone, all over. No pasts. And we're giving ourselves a rest; remember?

From each other.

"Suddenly –." Sorry, could we leave it there?

You said it.

Please. This is interesting, this political aspect.

I'm still trying to work out how we can get ourselves out of here in one piece.

Three pieces.

The political aspect has nothing to do with the emperor.

Quiet! Again!

But all right. "Suddenly, soon after his last visit to Maximilian, Strigel finds the tide of history washing right to his doorstep, and will have to make some important decisions."

Whose side was he on? That's what I can't stop wondering.

"He is in Vienna, at the imperial court, at the very beginning of the 1520s. By the time he gets back to Memmingen, things there have changed. The Swiss priest at the main church of St Martin's, Christoph Schappeler, who has previously been admonished by the civic authorities for his radical sermons, is now being encouraged. We have to remember that Memmingen was a free imperial city, which meant it owed allegiance to no local aristocrat, only to the emperor directly."

Who?

"The governing magistrates, supporting Schappeler, stay with him when he is excommunicated in 1524. By doing so, they effectively give their assent to the Protestant Reformation. What they surely do not realize, however, is that they thereby open the door to revolution. If people can change the way their spiritual lives are to be organized and directed, they can do the same where their social lives are concerned. Hierarchies, even ancient, need not last for ever."

Your friend.

"Early the next year, 1525, Schappeler the pastor, formerly Schappeler the priest, gets together with a writer-furrier in the town, Sebastian Lotzer, to draft what they call 'The Twelve Articles: The Just and Fundamental Articles of All the Peasantry and Tenants of Spiritual and Temporal Powers by Whom They Think Themselves Oppressed'. And their work is published as a pamphlet, with a print run of twenty-five thousand copies – an extraordinary number to be floating around, especially when one considers this was quite an inflammatory document.

"Oddly enough, the printing presses of Memmingen are making more than one mark on history at the time, for it is here in 1519 that a book is published with a certain word making its first appearance in print: 'America'."

Relevant?

"The Schappeler-Lotzer tract is probably being written and published in March 1525, when several peasant leaders and their followers are assembled in Memmingen. And it, too, contains a novel term – novel, at least, in the way it is being used: 'frey'. 'Free'. In the third of their articles, the peasants' spokesmen dare to affirm: 'It accords with Scripture that we are free and wish to be.' And here we see how the Reformation principle of open access to the Bible opens the way to social change. What Schappeler and Lotzer mean by 'free', if we read the context, is that nobody is to be classed as the property of another. However, this word 'free' seems to alarm them as soon as they utter it, and, as if shying at their own audacity, they immediately take a step back: 'Not that we want to be totally free and have no authority above us.'"

Leave him out of this.
Shut! Up!

"Our two authors, their eyes widened by the originality of what they are contemplating, see forward to what unbridled freedom may come to mean in a world that has lost not only universal religion but also, stumbling slowly but inexorably after it, universal morality."

I can't see any stars any more.

"In this schedule from sixteenth-century Memmingen – among demands that everyone should have access to woodland to gather timber and firewood, and so on – we find the first tentative testing of what it might be like to have all people treated as equal, the earliest bill of human rights, recognized as such three centuries and more later by Friedrich Engels."

There's one.

"Looking for some limit to the new freedom they are
proposing, Lotzer and Schappeler hit on a body
already in place: the board of magistrates, the
city's council or senate. And perhaps this could
only be happening in a place like Memmingen,
which has no local ruler. Authority lies, rather,
with people who have been elected – elected no
doubt by only a segment of the population, one
that does not include women and may be limited
in other ways, too, but nevertheless elected, not
attaining their precedence merely by their place
in some family that has been ruling since before
anyone could remember. Memmingen, where the
primacy of the emperor is entirely nominal, is
already a miniature republic. There needs only a
minor revolution to make it a people's democracy
– or as much of one as was thinkable at the time.
Just a gentle push."

Gone now.

"The upshot, however, is not the New Jerusalem but
war, the Peasants' War, which brings about battles
that are massacres, the peasant armies slaughtered
by far better armed, far better trained soldiery,

and all the peasant leaders, including some who were in Memmingen that early spring, dead by the end of the summer, either among the fallen or executed. And, to go on from what I pointed out before, we can hardly fail to observe how quickly all this unfolds after – it's tempting to say 'from' – the Reformation, and once more in Germany. In October 1517, Martin Luther hammers his Ninety-Five Theses to the church door in Wittenberg; seven and a half years later, Lotzer and Schappeler publish their Twelve Articles in Memmingen. Two phases of the same dawn. If the soul owes its allegiance not to priest, bishop and pope but directly to God, then so should the whole self, this individual self, newly identified and valued, that has made the Reformation possible and is waiting now for political enfranchisement."

How much longer?

So Luther would have supported the peasants?

Shush!

You'd think so, and at first he does. However, he rapidly changes his mind, and publishes a pamphlet of his own, entitled "Against the Murderous and Thieving Hordes of Peasants".

You know, the fellow in the tomb. If he's still there. When he was alive, I mean. Did either of you ever see him when he was alive?

Martin Luther?

No.

The same.

No!
Not much to talk about there then, is there?

"Strigel by now is in his mid-sixties and a respected member of the civic hierarchy. We can presume he follows the changing positions the city magistrates take, with regard to the Reformation at any rate."

You, suggest another topic.

What about the peasants? What about the Twelve
    Articles?

*Can't think of one. My mind's gone blank with all this
    waiting. Before, see, we were waiting with some
    purpose in mind – or purposes. We'd been told
    to. We were guarding the tomb. We were looking
    around to see if anyone might be approaching. We
    were listening for some sign. There was some danger
    in it, anticipation. We had to be alert.*

Anyway, that's our story.

*We had to be alert. Now, though, it's all over. It
    happened. We were supposed to stop it, but we didn't,
    so it happened.*

"As to his political beliefs and commitments, we can
    have no certainty. But consider for a moment: he
    is effectively a member of the growing middle class.
    What will it mean for him to express solidarity
    with a cause that is not his own? What good can
    it possibly do? How will any gesture of support,
    coming from such a direction, be regarded by the
    peasants and their leaders? The sides have been
    drawn, but a bourgeois artist is on neither one of
    them."

Have you finished?

"No certainty", you say. There are no letters, other
documents, I take it?

None.

In that case, what about his work, his paintings? Are
you suggesting –

Sorry.

If you'll let me go on.

Sorry.

"There may yet be something we can infer from his
work. He did not long survive the swivelling
of the religious compass in Memmingen from
Catholicism to Protestantism. That happened in
1521, and he died in 1528. But in those last seven
years, so we believe, he turned aside from religious
subjects to concentrate on portraits, images of the
new individual self."

Either of you want to play a game?

For the selves who could pay.

I give up. With you two, there's no such thing as silence.

Not only. Our four lads are not from among the wealthy. "The models for our four paintings – and we surely must assume there were models – were not paying to have themselves painted, and yet the artist treats them with as much care as any of his grand patrons. I would even say: with more. That he does not make them entirely recognizable – that he withholds much of the face in each case – is even part of the point. They are at once individual and general. They are simple humanity. They are common people. For the first time in the history of western art, a painter is making such a person the subject of a portrait. These are the first labourers as well as the first sleepers. They are not grandees, commanding attention with a gaze; their eyes are closed. They are ordinary people, at rest. One of them might work at a boot shop, another keep a vegetable patch. The new freedom, glimpsed in a document from the identical place and time, has been achieved. Strigel has painted it."

I said: Anyone want to play a game?

Could I play devil's advocate here? You might argue

that Strigel's turn from religious painting to portraiture was a response to the market. With the coming of Protestantism, images of the Virgin enthroned in gilded architecture were not going to be needed any more. Rising affluence at the same time meant that portraits were.

Not now.

Yes, but Catholicism survived in Memmingen, alongside the new dispensation, and that's directly relevant to these paintings. "This is not to forget that our paintings are at the same time religious images. We believe Strigel painted them for the church of Our Lady in Memmingen in 1521-2."

Maybe later.

"This was the second church of the town, and its incumbent was a conservative. Did our painter accept the commission out of sympathy with the old Catholic ritual? Did he see, at the same time, an opportunity to convey fellow feeling with the ordinary fellow? Was he, in other words, on both sides at once?"

You?

"Since we are dealing with panel paintings, he would not necessarily have had to be on site; he could have supplied them from anywhere. However, it is simplest to assume that, now back in his home town, he was able to walk through the streets to the church for which he was working, look around the interior in a way he perhaps had not before, judge the light in which his paintings would be seen. Or perhaps that did not matter so much to him. Perhaps his theory of representation was closer to that of an icon painter, that the image contained a presence independent of the conditions under which it might be viewed. It was there. Therefore what it showed was there. We do not know. How could we?"

No.

"Let us follow him as he enters the church in which his paintings are going to be displayed."

Fun buddies you two are.

"Coming from whatever direction, he enters the church. Stands in the emptiness. The light. The bulk of silence. He has come a little ahead of a meeting he is to have with one of the priests, to discuss the commission."

Might as well be –

"He wants to renew his acquaintance with the place."

All right, then. What do you have in mind?

"He looks around."

Either of you got some dice?

"On the walls are sequences of images painted in the last century – fifteenth-century graphic novels. The life of the Virgin, and so on."

No.

"We do not know, but he knows, as he goes, something of who painted what in these fresco cycles. Crude but appealing, they evoke for him a feeling he cannot tell whether to call affection or dismay."

Me neither.

"Those figures were pointed out to him when he was a boy as his grandfather's work."

Anything to write on? Or with?

"Do you remember your grandfather? The question would be put to him now and again, and he would gently nod, because a nod could not be counted a lie."

Neither.

"'How far we have come.' The thought stays in his head, of course. He does not speak."

Nor me.

"The only sound is that of his footsteps, which more engender than disturb the resonant stillness."

Knucklebones?

"We do not know, but he knows, because this, too, was pointed out to him, with whatever mixture of pride and amusement, what his father and his uncle contributed as teenage apprentices in their father's workshop."

What did you say?

"A background here."

Knucklebones.

"Before that the colouring-in of a robe."

No.

"Later a face."

What?

"A whole figure."

Knucklebones.

"That apostle had been an attempt at a portrait of the
   cheesemonger. You could still see the resemblance,
   though this was all of thirty years ago now."

No, I don't.

"He takes careful, cogitative steps. He breathes in the
   cold morning air, the scent of damp and stone
   mould. He contemplates, measuring in his mind,
   the niche in which his four paintings will be
   positioned."

Anybody got any other ideas?

"There is something else about these watchkeepers
   being painted, that their motionlessness – their
   necessary motionlessness, in the most banal sense,
   as being made of shape and pigment on wood – is
   naturalistic, true to their existence. They are like
   this. They have been like this for some while. They
   will be like this for some while yet. Their early
   morning will outlast us."

Ideas about what?

"But before we leave this church in Memmingen, and
    Strigel pacing its interior, we should consider the
    purpose of his commission."

A game we could all play.

Yes?

Nothing comes to mind.

I don't want to go on with this.

*What? Sorry, I missed what you said. I was thinking
    about something else.*

Please.

About what?

Please.

I asked if any of us had any other ideas.

"These paintings…. These four paintings are to play a part in an annual re-enactment. There is an actual model tomb for them to guard, built into the floor of the church, or into a wall. On Good Friday evening the body – what is believed to constitute the body, namely a consecrated wafer – is placed in the tomb, which is closed with a stone block or lid and perhaps then sealed, after which the four painted figures are stationed round about to stand watch. Asleep. Then on Easter morning the body – the wafer – is brought out again, surely with much ceremony. What was dead and gone is alive and present. The guardians are put away for next year."

A game we could play, since none of us has any dice, or knucklebones, or anything to write with.

I know. I heard that much.

Well, do you have any other ideas?

"They are actors in a play, actors whose part is to sleep throughout the proceedings. I cannot think of many plays in which that happens."

No.

And leave me out of it, all right? All you want to do is talk, talk, talk! I'm sick of it!

It was just something to pass the time. That's all –

Give it a rest! That's all I ask. Give it a rest. The time will pass whatever we do. Or else it won't.

"We beat the Gaulies –"

Shut up, will you!

Don't mind him. He's in one of his moods. Go on. I like this one.

"We beat the Gaulies up the Rhône,
  And then we beat them back."

Shut up, I said!

Leave him alone! Some of us are enjoying the song. If you don't want to hear it you can go and bury yourself. There's a tomb over there waiting for an occupant.

"But Reformation and revolution are in the air as our painter's brushes skim the oak. He will be aware of the changes taking place around and within him. His contemporaries will, too. For them his images may still contain and convey the real presence of real people – in this case, the only people who, though unaware, are there at the event crucial to the governing belief system of most of Europe. Yet these identities are draining from them, as holes are punctured in that belief system. They are becoming what they also are: contemporary individuals."

"Our general said: Leave them alone!"

"Probably for many people of the time, looking at these paintings as they stand sleeping guard through Holy Saturday, there is a flickering between these two realities: they are the Roman soldiers at the tomb, and they are four fellows such as you might see any day on the street. Looking for models, Strigel might go first to men doing the same job, the town watch, who can be portrayed in their own clothing and pieces of armour, and with their own weapons, so that the fellow townspeople who are the first audience might well recognize, in the painted watchmen, the watchmen they know – even the one in the circular hat that completely obscures his features, just as they will see, at a performance of a play, the actors as well as the characters, the two simultaneously."

Give it a rest!
"And then he said: Attack!"

"They are the tomb guardians. They are, as people can see, the tomb guardians."

"We charged, they held, we charged, they turned,"

"And in the same instant they are ordinary men, such as you see serving in a shop or, indeed, tramping the streets at night, on patrol.

"And then we heard a cry."

"Now, in being painted, these fellows are ennobled, even as they engage in what is not a very ennobling activity, namely sleeping."

"They flung their weapons to the ground,"

"They exude repose."

"And waved their hands sky high."

"They are at rest."

"Our general strode up to their chief –"

"Observe the muted colour schemes."

That's enough! Enough! This is all ancient history!

"The day is just beginning, but this could equally be
    twilight, the soft brown of twilight in the country,
    where men who have worked hard physically
    through the day turn to rest."

Oh, excuse me; if you please.

"To the extent that these are the first single portraits
    of people from the labouring class, we are indeed
    present at a dawn."

Let him alone. He wasn't doing any harm.

"And it is here, in this silence, that Strigel is recording
    his position with regard to the brewing social
    emergency. 'We are free', these four declare
    – except that they do not have to declare it. They
    have it. Freedom. They are full of it."

It's all right. No point arguing with him. I just won't sing any more. All the fun's gone out of it, anyway.

Excuse me.

Yes?

They are not serfs, they are not bondsmen, I grant you. But is that all your Memmingen revolutionaries were proposing?

There's always someone'll spoil everything.

They have taken a step.

They're armed.

Their newfound freedom needs protecting.

And on whose behalf are they going to raise those arms of theirs when, in a very short time, the peasants rebel against the lords, and armed men, presumably trained, are going to be wanted by both camps?

Too right.

Strigel doesn't say. This is idyll. This is not then, nor is it now. It is ever and always. "Being asleep, the figures are reduced, or I would rather say elevated, to the level of common humanity. None of us can choose how we sleep. Remember: one of these fellows has his mouth open, and would probably not have elected to be shown that way if he had had any decision in the matter. So has the artist thereby taken advantage of him, even betrayed him? No, not at all. In giving him sleep, and even in making it so that his dignity slips, Strigel gives him something far above personal dignity, enfolds him in the human race. Imagine how this is happening in the studio. Strigel has called in the Memmingen watch; these four might be the entire corps. Having been up all night, they are indeed sleepy, for the painter has had them come here in the daytime, because painting is done by daylight, and if these pictures are being prepared for Easter they are perhaps being done in February or early March, when the hours of daylight are relatively few, so that work must be done in the middle of the day, when these men would normally be in their beds. They might yawn. They well might yawn. The artist is instantaneously seized by this small image of an aperture surrounded by beard. Yes, that. He places the men in position, in this former stable, with its high, wide double doors open to let in the light, and one of them is lying on the fresh straw with his knees up, and another – the one with the great wheel of a hat, which might be his own or one the artist, who has a store of such odd accoutrements, has given him for the occasion, to shield his face thoroughly – sitting, and another, the one with the beard, around a mouth that will hang open in his picture, also sitting, he being the one to be shown supporting that bearded face on his upturned left palm, these last two sitters, sitters in two senses, both having their knees raised in the sketches the artist makes on a sanded pine board, with shorthand notes of colours and volumes, for he will have the men here in position – has the bearded one really dozed off? – only for an hour or so, then send them home to bed, with a coin in their fists, and get on with working up the paintings that will keep them alive for centuries."

Well?

"Them": the models or the tomb guardians?

Well what?

Both. Both remain.

Well, are we going to stay here forever?

You got any better ideas?

I'm scared.

Me too.

I'm tired and I'm scared, but I'm more scared than I am tired, and just staying on here like this isn't helping.

Isn't helping.

Let's face it, the job's over. We can't claim we're still guarding anything.

We don't know that.

Come on!

No, we don't know that, not for certain.

You want to go and take a look? Or you do? All right, then. Neither do I. And anyway, we don't need to look, do we? Why would they re-open the tomb if they weren't going to put something in, which makes no sense at all, or – wait for it – take something out. And what were they going to take out?

The body?

Thank you! Well done! The body. What we were supposed to be guarding. Not letting person or persons un-known steal it away from under our noses.

Which they have done.

Probably.

"The kind of small-scale re-enactment I spoke of – the Easter garden for which the paintings were made – seem to have been made, I should say – well, that was not the only kind of dramatic representation of the event going on at the time. The whole story would also be presented by living actors, local townspeople, on a stage in their church or out of doors."

Which they have done. Ergo, we now have no function.

"I refer, of course, to passion plays."

But we can't go.

"No such play from Memmingen is recorded, but a lot were never written down. So there could have been a Memminger Passionspiel, and perhaps even a local tradition that the members of the town watch would play the guardians at the tomb. Strigel's models, in his studio, will therefore find themselves acting familiar roles: playing themselves playing themselves pretending to sleep. The painter, meanwhile, sees a different multiplicity. He is all at once looking at these members of the town watch, paying the closest, finest attention to the lie of a leg or the texture of a jerkin, fully in the actual, and simultaneously thinking both of Roman legionaries and of characters in a play."

All right, what are our choices?

"Strigel is a traveller. If there was, after all, no passion play regularly acted out in Memmingen, he may well have seen one somewhere, quite possibly in Vienna, where he stayed a couple of years."

Rule out staying here any longer.

"And Vienna, remember, is the capital of the empire, of the Holy Roman Empire. Quite apart from any passion play taking place there, memories of the first century are being cherished not only in a name but also by way of the artefacts that Maximilian and his predecessors had gathered around themselves to bolster their claim of continuity with Augustus. Based on what he has seen, Strigel could give his legionaries an 'authentic' look."

Too much longer.

"Why, then, does he not give them Roman breast-
plates, Roman helmets, Roman greaves, Roman
weapons?"

Rule out going back to the camp.

"Because he is concerned not with antiquarianism
but with truth, and the truth of this moment is
that the tomb guardians, the tomb guardians, are
here."

Oh?

"Let us consider a little further the passion plays of this
same period. There was a long tradition in the
western church of having the gospel story read
out at Easter mass by several people in character
– the Latin text, of course, so this would be
done by monks or priests. Out of that came the
passion play, elaborating the bare thread of the
gospel accounts into rich cloth, and presenting
everything in the vernacular, in the language of
the people. Liturgy spun into popular entertain-
ment. The whole thing has now escaped the clerics;
it is in the hands of tradespeople in the growing

cities. There is comedy in these shows, and much else that you will not find in the Bible."

I'm not sure I want to give up on that.

"Then they were snuffed out by the double clamp of the Reformation and the Counter-Reformation, both Protestant clergy and Catholic acting to enforce church control of spiritual life – in a word, to professionalize religion. The props and costumes were put away, the words forgotten. Only the occasional script preserved the memory."

Nor me. We're soldiers. That's our life.

"Losses of variants, however, do not matter too much, because our concern is with the tomb guardians' presence in the plays, not with what they say."

If we went back, we'd have to have a story, and we can't think of one.

"Strigel, if we can imagine him watching one of these plays, has an idea. He sees the whole thing being done on a smaller scale, with pictures and models.

He then persuades his church of Our Lady to be a home for it, enable him to realize what we might call an installation."

Should we think again?
What's the use?

"Coming from the fifteenth century, nearly all the surviving scripts agree with that century's painters that there were four tomb guardians. The Chester play skips the norm in having three. One missing, as it were."

If nothing else, we don't know what he might have said.

Do they have names?

Or not said.

Sometimes. One of the English plays has them as Ameraunt, Arfaxat, Cosdram and Affraunt, names surely chosen to sound exotic. To add to the effect these fellows invoke Saint Mahound, or Muhammad, of course. Never mind the anachronism.

At least the writer was going for the right part of the world.

Yes, but that raises the question of whether the Romans made it a policy to station soldiers on their home turf, which would have made communication with the native population easier, for sure, but would have run the risk of divided loyalties, or whether they had their legionaries serving as far away as possible: Welshmen in Judæa, Thracians on Hadrian's Wall. Maybe they would also have put men from different places together, so that they couldn't talk too much among themselves and cause trouble.

Tell you the truth, I was looking for a change of scene.

Me too.

But I'm not going until we have a good sound plan.

"With their strange names and their invocation of Mahound, they are presented as not only alien but hostile, which is how they appear, too, in so many of the period's paintings: uncouth, undignified, with skewed expressions. This is how they must look, and this is how they must speak, being soldiers dispatched by Pilate, pawns of an archenemy."

Of course.

"Strigel, of course, shows them as ordinary lads in a
        peaceable landscape, given the levelling grace of
        sleep. And yet their quiet, plain humanity is there
        in the plays too – as perhaps it has to be, given
        that the tomb guardians are, though enemy agents,
        also messengers of divine miracle. Remember
        Matthew: 'some of the watch came into the city,
        and shewed unto the chief priests all the things
        that were done.'"

We could go to their priests.

Some of them?

And say what?

So it says.

They never liked him.

Not all?

Him who?

No. Already a separation.

Him in the tomb. Him that was in the tomb. They never liked him. They'd help us out.

Going back to Matthew: "'And when they were assembled with the elders, and had taken counsel, they gave large money unto the soldiers, Saying, Say ye, His disciples came by night, and stole him away while we slept. And if this come to the governor's ears, we will persuade him, and secure you.'" You see what this means?

Maybe yes, maybe no.

That they told their story only in the hope of reward, which undermines their reliability as witnesses. But also that the whole story of the sleeping soldiers is a fiction, concocted by these "elders".

They don't like us, either.

Might be a fiction. Just because the tomb guardians
were told to say they'd been asleep doesn't mean
they hadn't in fact been asleep.

It's an idea, though.
We'd be idiots.
They might give us some help.

The Judæan headmen pay them to deny the event,
give them an alternative story, that they'd been
asleep, and promise to square things with Pilate.
If the tomb guardians really had nodded off, these
native leaders were suddenly solving all their problems for them, and handing them cash into the
bargain.

We'd be idiots.

You say all this in the lecture?
More or less.

*All right, give us a better idea. Or do you want to go back
to the camp?*

Please go on, then.

"The plays, though, with no Biblical authority whatso-
ever, go for the more straightforward and probable
story that the tomb guardians go first to their
commander, to Pilate."

Can't do that.
Too right we can't.

"In some of the plays they tell Pilate they were terrified
by what they were witnessing. Never – and this
is hardly too surprising – do they say they slept
through it all."

Which leaves us with what, exactly?

"Yet in every one of the plays this seems to be what is
happening. Some say nothing about the tomb
guardians sleeping. However, in these scripts they
have no lines as the event is taking place, and so
we can imagine they must have been presented as
sleeping. They start to talk again when it is all over,
and they notice, of course, what has happened.
And though there is nothing specific to say they
have suddenly woken up, that must be how the

scene was acted. Others have an angel arriving to cast a spell of sleep on the four soldiers. There's also a play in which the tomb guardians hear before that from a different stranger, now one of their own: a night watchman."

We take off from here. We'll find someone who'll give us a hand.

"'Well-arm̀èd knights and bold,' he begins."

What if we don't? We're not living in a fairy story.

Knights?

"Ritter" in the original. Like Strigel, those who put together the plays weren't after historical accuracy. Their dramas are set in contemporary feudal, chivalric Europe.

Maybe not. But I'm starting to wonder if this isn't a dream we're all having.

"'Well-arm̀èd knights and bold, Think now of the gold, That has been promised you.' This night watchman undertakes to help them stay awake by making his call, but then we have the angel lulling them to sleep: 'Sleep, you guardians of the tomb, Now for God you must make room.'"

Wake up...

Not exactly the shock and awe that Matthew wrote of.

No, my friend, it's not a dream. I can feel the glare in my eye from the sun coming up over there. I can stamp my foot and feel the solid ground. I can talk to you and hear my voice as I do so. This is reality all right, like it or not.

As you say.
Go on, then.

We should get out of here, like I said.

I'm afraid that's it. That's as far as I've got. Thank you for listening, anyway. I didn't think I could get through it.

Ready when you are.
Hang on!

No, thank you. But come on, whatever made you say
this lecture's falling apart?

Yes?

The fact that it is, that it has. Well and truly. I can't go
on with it. And I can't go back to it.
I don't understand.

Shouldn't we first of all decide where we're aiming for?

York. I went to York.

*And how long do you think we're going to last out there
anyway?*

York?

He's got a point.

It's where the other painting is, the fourth one, the one that got separated from the three that ended up in Munich. They were all together in 1622, when they were mentioned in a will. Then we lose sight of them. Munich got their three in 1935, from a dealer, by which time the other one was in the possession of an English connoisseur, Lycett Green. He left his collection to the York Art Gallery.

We'll survive. We're armed.

You went there to see it?

They don't have it on display, but they were very helpful, and, yes, I saw it.

And?

It wasn't what I was expecting.

Great.

In what way?

Look: I'll get him up on the screen for you. See? This fellow's more grandly dressed, for a start. And he doesn't seem so fully asleep: he has the fingers of one hand wrapped tight around that staff. Also, he's looking more towards the viewer. And he's facing the other way, to the left.

Now that you say...

They also showed me some documentation I hadn't seen before.

Enlightening?

That would be one way of putting it. I knew that a certain Hans Rott, who made a study in the 1930s of archives relating to works of art in this part of Germany, found records of payments made to Strigel in the year 1521-2 on account of a "grab", a grave or tomb. And I knew that Ernst Buchner, who had acquired the three panels for Munich, then made the connection with this commission – which is why the Munich catalogue has them as "Grabwächter", tomb guardians. York, however, lists its picture as "Sleeping Soldier", on account of a letter they received from a third German scholar, Edeltraud Rettich. She cast doubt on the paintings as images of the tomb guardians. And we have to take her view seriously, because she was – and remains – the leading authority on Strigel.

What was her case?

Principally that there's no documentary evidence.

Would we expect any?

What about you, then? Are you with me?

Probably not. But there are other things we can see for ourselves. The fact that the York soldier is facing the other way, for instance. If the four had been made as a set, you'd expect them all to face the same way, or two one way and two the other.

Not necessarily. Artistic caprice. But also, Strigel could have wanted this one to stand out, in his dress as well as his positioning, because he's the officer in charge.

'Fraid not, pal.

Then, most of them have at least some part of their footwear cut off. They've obviously been interfered with. And that's the only reason they're the same size, which is the only reason they look like a group. They could have been cut out of a larger picture that had nothing to do with the tomb guardians.

Perhaps. But we can think of other possible explanations. For one thing, that re-enactment in that church could have gone on being played out for decades, and the edges of the paintings gotten worn. Or if they were stuffed in a cupboard, they could have fallen prey to the worm.

I'm on my own, then?

Possible, yes. But listen: What about this one? – And I can't think why it didn't occur to me before. – There's no tomb.

What?

There's no tomb. If these are the tomb guardians, where's the tomb they're supposed to be guarding? You'd have imagined Strigel would have put in a corner of masonry or something. But there's nothing to place these fellows – nothing, therefore, to identify them.

Wait: they were made to stand guard around a model tomb, you said. Strigel didn't need to indicate in his paintings that they're at a tomb, because there it was, in solid stone. Any bit of painted tomb would have spoiled the effect. We've got to understand these paintings in terms of their original purpose – in terms of that installation you talked about.

You're not going anywhere.

Again, possible, but we've lost all certainty.

But –

Let me go on! These four were my life. For years.
And still there was so much I wanted to say to
them. If they'd been here, I could have done that
– never mind that they wouldn't have been able to
respond. I could have said they're the only human
beings right there, at exactly the right moment,
and they're missing the event. I could have said
their sleep is an admonishment to us, who also
sleep through so much. I could have said their
sleep is a challenge to us, to wake up. I could have
told them that, even though they're bit players,
almost the least of bit players, unmentioned in
three gospels out of four, and sleeping through
what they alone might have witnessed, even so
their silent testimony means something to us. I
could have told them they have the luck to live at a
time when belief was as everyday as bread. I could
have said they cannot be expected to comprehend
us, for whom the testimony of the least of bit
players may be as much as we can accept. I could
have said their sleep is honour, for they are near to
divinity as it happens. I could have said their sleep
is anxiety, that it is fear, and that it is sorrow. I
could have said they sleep in anxiety for us, whose
language so reluctantly moves into prayer or
permits the voice of blessing. I could have said they

sleep in fear for us who cannot reach the ground within ourselves. I could have said they sleep in sorrow for us who sleep through so many levels of our lives. I could have told them we hear them, as in their sleep, in their silence, they tell us that we, too, are guarding a tomb. We don't know what's in it. Perhaps nothing. Perhaps what was once in it has gone. We're scared to look. But we go on guarding it. I could have said all this, but now –

Now I understand. You can't be absolutely sure who these figures are. It's possible Strigel didn't paint them as the tomb guardians. It's possible that'll be proved one day. The certainty's gone, as you say. But that's exactly what you just said distinguishes our age from theirs. We can't go back, or pretend that we are back. We have to go on from where we are. In doubt. These four painted sleepers – innocent sleepers, you said – are windows. Through each of these windows we can see someone from twenty centuries ago, someone who had an important job to do and didn't do it, someone whose sleep and awakening mirrored on a mundane human level what was taking place right there behind them. The windows have been polished with so much looking. One day, sure, they may close over. But they haven't done so yet. And see: this fourth one, this last one, I think his eyes are open a tiny bit.

It's him!

Where?

Down there, at the bottom of the hill.

I think you're right.

I know I'm right. It's him. Large as life.

I wonder where he's been.

We'll know soon enough.

It's him. He's coming back.

Gemeinschaft

The publication of this book was assisted by the following supporters on Unbound:

MACES & HALBERDS

Linda Shorey • Patrick Ozzard-Low • Debra Chatfield • Nicolas Hodges • Wendy Whidden • Michael Caines • Tom Moody-Stuart Arthur Schiller • Steve Walsh • Richard Furniss • Bernard Moxham David Robins • Christine Anthony • Esme Pears • Gavin Plumley Mary Sherwood Brock • Kate Boulton

PIKES & CROSSBOWS

Andrea Barlien • Graham Fulcher • Cindy Haiken • Luke Lewis Rick Whitaker • John Mitchinson • Nick Breeze • Darrin Britting Tilmann Böttcher • Angie Creed • Richard Faria • Lionel Friend Jonathan Cross • David Hebblethwaite • Tina Pelikan • Louise Duchesneau • Kevin Raftery • Matthew Gurewitsch • Peter McMullin Trevor Bača • Taylor Davis-Van Atta • Hugh Hudson • Alan Teder Carali McCall • Evalyn Lee • Dawn Baird • Keith Mantell • Justin Gau • William Eaves • Jim O'Brien • Jeff Tompkins • Paul Fulcher Sam Wigglesworth • Neil George • Ian Hagues • Antony Peattie Claire Allen • Constance Repplier • Jacquie Knott • Alice Broadribb Melissa De Groff • E R Andrew Davis • Chiara Libero • Patric ffrench Devitt • Heather Binsch • Linda Monckton • Nathan Munday Belle Claudi • Keith Mantell • Wendy Watson • John Link • Declan O'Driscoll • Kevin Davey • Margaret Jones • Emanuel Overbeeke Kimberly Dunster • Xak Bjerken • Gregory Kindall • David Ward • Eddie Kohler • Sally Groves • Robert Worby • John Fallas Camille Webb • Fred Porter • Toby Ann Cronin

About the Author

Paul Griffiths is an internationally respected music critic and librettist. His books have been translated into eleven languages.

He has worked as a music critic on major publications (*The Times*, *The New Yorker*, *The New York Times*). He received an OBE for services to music literature and composition, and has been honoured also in France (Chevalier dans l'Ordre des Arts et des Lettres) and the United States (Member of the American Academy of Arts and Sciences). Excerpts from his third novel *let me tell you* were collected in *The Penguin Book of Oulipo.*

Mr. Beethoven was short-listed for The Goldsmiths Prize 2020, and longlisted for The Walter Scott Prize and Republic of Consciousness Prize in 2021.